My Purpose Pathway
Student Portfolio

Written in collaboration with Progressive Bridges, Inc., 2015

Pursue Your Purpose, Not Your Dreams

Table of Contents

My Purpose Pathways
Leadership Portfolio

Introduction:

The ***My Purpose Pathways* Leadership Portfolio** kept throughout the lessons will help you document your knowledge and understanding of the principles presented in the authors' vignettes and how they relate to you and your life. It is also a way for you to explore your own thoughts related to your personal growth toward leadership through self-reflection, written responses to positive quotes, research-related project planning, personal journal entries, personal goal setting, and more!

Assessments:

A **Pre and Post Assessment**, a simple method of measuring growth of student knowledge throughout the program, is included in the Facilitator Guide.

The **My Purpose Checklist** can be made available for daily use as a self-assessment and/or teacher assessment throughout the program. Students can view at a glance the My Purpose leadership behaviors that are needed for success. Having students complete the checklist builds self-awareness, self-esteem, and growth.

The **My Purpose Rubric** is available for daily use by students with persistent behavior challenges. Both students and teachers can rate the exhibition of proactive My Purpose leadership behaviors and measure over time the increase in positive behaviors evident in school and supplemental educational settings.

Pursue Your Purpose, Not Your Dreams

Wise Words Practice Activities

Word Sorts: Organize all of the vocabulary words into groupings that have common characteristics. Make up as many grouping titles as needed to go with the groupings. Think of a creative way to portray your Word Sort.

Word Map: Draw a map of the following information all hooked to the center (the vocabulary word): synonyms, antonyms, definition, part of speech, other word forms, used in a sentence from the text, used in your own sentence, visual sketch.

Symbolize It: Choose 5 wise words from your chapter list. Construct a picture, graphic, or symbol for each word that captures to meaning of the word.

SCUBA Diving with Vocabulary:

      a. S – **Sound** it out. Say the whole word to yourself a couple of times.

      b. C – **Check** the clues in the sentence and paragraph and think about what word would fit best in place of the unknown word.

      c. U – **Use** the text's main idea to make a good guess for the word's meaning.

      d. B – **Break** the word into parts that have meanings that you recognize, and/or think of similar words.

      e. A – **Ask** for help from a peer or teacher, or use the internet.

Wise Word Debate: Use at least 5 words meaningfully in a written debate supporting your position about any current topic in today's news. Be sure your debate or argument makes sense.

Wise Words

Lesson 1	Lesson 2	Lesson 3	Lesson 4
Dreamed	Distinctions	Professional	Pessimist
Gravitated	Destined	Influence	Barrier
Stressed	Jeopardized	Internally	Hurdle
Counseling	Burnout	Coolness	Obstacle
Reflections	Gratification	Befriend	Impediment
Focus	Regrets	Portrayal	Courage
Academically	Misinterpretation	Perceptions	Tenacity
Devastating	Devastating	Evaluate	Repel
Transformation	Pursue	Re-Define	
Networking		Motivational	

Lesson 5	Lesson 6	Lesson 7	Lesson 8
Unforseen	Acknowledge	Maximizing	Rebuilding
Capability	Potential	Potential	Dismantle
Commitment	Reputation	Recognize	Transitioning
Dysfunctional	Pressure	Unfulfilled	Reassemble
Internal	Considered	Destruction	Exposing
Paralyze	Dimensional	Reputation	Academically
Rational	Satisfaction	Distinct	Committing
Perceived	Anxious	Perspective	Potential
Fortunate	Conquering	Identity	Engaged
Jeopardized	Distress	Situational	Attempted

Lesson 9	Lesson 10	Lesson 11	Lesson 12
Heterosexism	Inherited	Translate	Possibility
Interactions	Mastered	Possibilities	Issues
Ableism	Sacrificing	Conditioned	Overshadows
Capacities	Franchise	Acceptance	Maturity
Sexism	Encouragement	Phrases	Purposefully
Superiority	Presence	Journey	Guidance
Covert	Progressing	Pressure	Mental
Overt	Aligned	Interpretation	Concerned
Racism	Mindful	Role	Circumstances
Microaggressions	Accountable	Passion	Syndrome
Classism			

Pursue Your Purpose, Not Your Dream

Lesson 1   INTRODUCTION

Lesson Focus: This lesson will help you start thinking about things that you like to do and why you like to do them. It will also introduce you to the author of this book. As you begin to think through these ideas, you will prepare to read and understand yourself better as you start reading the entire book.

Wise Word Work: Complete one of the Wise Words activities on page 5.

How does it feel to have a dream to do something for so long, only to not be able to actually make it come true?

_____

_____

Before you read Chapter 1, what do you think is the difference between your purpose and your dreams?

_____

_____

_____

Character Web:

Complete a character web describing the author based on the introduction. Connect at least 10 details about the author to the shape below containing his name.

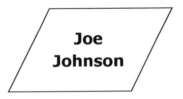

Based on the author's introduction of himself, why do you think he chose this title for his book?

_____
_____
_____
_____
_____

What Brings You Joy?

In 3 minutes, write down all of the jobs, large and small, you have ever had. Include volunteer work, work you have done for free, work you received an allowance for at home, service work, anything you can think of.

Look at your list and decide which things brought you the most joy.
Place a star by those items above. Consider things you absolutely loved!
Rewrite those starred items here:

Answer these questions about the tasks that brought you joy:

Which parts of these tasks did I absolutely love doing?

_____
_____
_____

Why did it bring me so much joy?

_____
_____
_____

Could I do it for free?

_____

Was I good at what I was doing?

_____
_____

Did others think I was good at what I was doing?

_____
_____

What do I think it is that makes me enjoy that task?

_____
_____

Explain 1 thing you want to take away from reading this book:

_____
_____
_____

Pursue Your Purpose, Not Your Dreams

Lesson 2   **PURPOSE vs DREAMS: WHAT DO YOU MEAN?**

Lesson Focus: Apply your understanding about the differences between dreams and personal purpose.

Wise Word Work: Complete one of the Wise Words activities on page 5.

Dreams vs. Purpose:

How does the author explain the differences between dreams and your purpose? (Some clues can be found on pages 20 & 21 of the text.) Place each clue below the appropriate box below.

PURPOSE	DREAM

What do you think is the biggest difference between a "purpose" and a "dream"?

_____

_____

_____

_____

What does this picture tell you about YOUR journey to your true purpose in life?

_____

_____

_____

_____

_____

_____

_____

_____

_____

_____

_____

_____

_____

_____

_____

_____

How would you describe your journey so far in finding your purpose? Illustrate it or describe it in 3 words below.

> ### "Be all that you can be."
> ### - Army Motto

Meaning of This Quote: Read the quote above. Do you think this quote refers to pursuing your purpose or your dreams? Explain your answer in detail.

_____
_____
_____
_____
_____
_____

WHO?? -- **That's ME!**

Place yourself on the line above with an X describing how well you know yourself today. Explain why you chose this placement. What do you think will move you closer to knowing your purpose and why?

_____
_____
_____

Clarify Your Values: Look at page 18 of the text. List 6 values from the list that describe you. Where do you think your values came from and why? Place a star next to those values you received from your family.

1. _____
2. _____
3. _____
4. _____
5. _____
6. _____

Matching Values & Actions: Choose 2 values above. For each value, write 3 actions that would match it.

Value: _____

3 Matching Actions:

_____   _____   _____

Value: _____

3 Matching Actions:

_____   _____   _____

Rate your current practice of matching your values & actions by placing an X on the line below indicating the level of match between your values & actions.

UNMATCHED-------------------------------PERFECTLY MATCHED

write a email/text as if you were explaining to a younger sibling about the important of matched values and actions.

_____

_____

_____

_____

_____

_____

_____

_____

_____

_____

_____

_____

_____

_____

Pursue Your Purpose, Not Your Dream

Lesson 3   WHAT IS YOUR COOL?

Lesson Focus: This lesson will focus on how family, friends and society impacts the idea of what "cool" really means.

Wise Word Work: Complete one of the Wise Words activities on page 5.

How "cool" are YOU? Place yourself (draw an X) on top of the continuum describing where you think society sees you. Now place a smiley face where you think of yourself on this continuum. Explain the differences and similarities on the lines below.

UNCOOL ---VERY COOL

_____

_____

_____

When redefining "cool", what 3 words should we live by?

_____   _____   _____

What I Think is COOL:

List 4 things/actions/people you think are "cool" and why they are cool on the lines below. Star the ones on which you think "society" would agree with you.

Cool Things: **Why It is Cool:**

_____   _____

_____   _____

_____   _____

_____   _____

Social Media Cool: Social media and what is trending plays a huge part in telling us what "cool" is at any given moment. Think of something "uncool" that social media might be able to turn into something "cool" with the right social media campaign. Design a social media campaign to turn something "uncool" into something "cool" in 30 days or less! Plan your strategy here and then create a video to explain and illustrate your social media campaign to others in your class. With a classmate, try your strategy for real to see what happens!

Create a lyrics to a rap or song about "cool" and how it changes continuously. Highlight lyrics within a powerpoint presentation so others can see how you made your point about "coolness" based on what you have read and learned in this chapter. (Extra points given for performances) Place your draft of lyrics here:

_____

_____

_____

_____

_____

_____

How "Cool" can Influence Dreams: How does society's view of what is "cool" impact your dreams? If you lived in a different country, do you think your dreams would be different? Why or why not?

_____

_____

_____

How "Cool" can Influence Purpose: How does society's view of what is "cool" impact your purpose? If you lived in a different country, do you think your purpose would be different? Why or why not?

_____

_____

_____

Draw a diagram illustrating how society's view of "cool" can influence dreams and purpose.

Pursue Your Purpose, Not Your Dream

Lesson 4   THE NEGATIVE THINGS IN YOUR LIFE!

Lesson Focus: Focus on the meaning of a negative mind and how one can live life by using positivity thinking. You should be able to demonstrate the impact of living life without focusing on the negative.

Wise Word Work: Complete one of the Wise Words activities on page 5.

Trace a Negative Thought: To understand the power of 1 negative thought, trace one of your own. Start at the first little negative thought or worry and track its path, thought by thought. Place each thought in a shape of the flowchart.

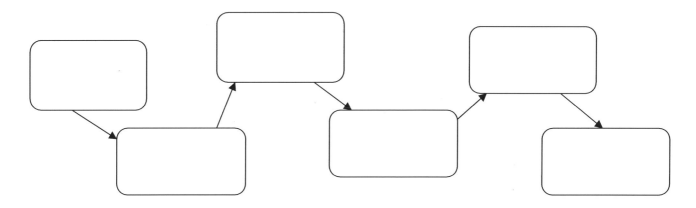

> **"You can't live a positive life with a negative attitude."**
>
> **- Unknown**

Explain this quote in your own words and give an example from your own life.

_____

_____

_____

_____

_____

How Do You Use Your Thought Time?

Think about your thoughts throughout the day. What percentage are positive thoughts and what percentage are negative thoughts? For one day, record your thoughts every 10 minutes while you are awake. Rather than recording words, simply place a + or a – next to the time. At the end of the day, count up your total marks. Count the number of + marks and the number of – marks. Find the percentage of time you had positive and negative thoughts by dividing the total marks by the number of + marks and the total marks by the number of – marks. Record your results below by filling in the circle based on the percentages you recorded. Each quarter represents 4 hours for a total of 16 waking hours in a day.

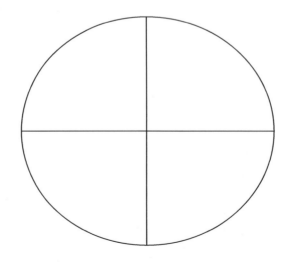

Were you surprised at your results? Why or why not?

_____

_____

Research the effects of negative thinking. Write 5 facts you discover about the impact of negative thinking. Place a star next to the 3 facts that surprised you most.

    1. _____

    2. _____

    3. _____

    4. _____

    5. _____

Plan to Reduce Negative Thinking:

Explain 3 ways you plan to reduce negative thinking every day.

    1. _____

    2. _____

    3. _____

Name an accountability partner that you can share your plan with who will remind you to stay on track.

Name: _____

When/How Often will You Check In: _____

Pursue Your Purpose, Not Your Dream

Lesson 5   **POSITIVE THINKING**

Lesson Focus: In this lesson, you will be able to understand how stressful situations in life can be impacted and changed with positive thinking. You will recognize how to get through rough times in life and use positive thoughts in this process.

Wise Word Work: Complete one of the Wise Words activities on page 5.

> "He who says he can and he who says he can't,
>
> are both right." - Confucious

Explain the meaning of this quote in your own words:

_____

_____

_____

_____

The Positive Thinking Starter Kit:

Ask yourself...

Did I wake up this morning?	Yes	No
Do I have 10 fingers and 10 toes?	Yes	No
Do I have clothes to put on?	Yes	No
Do I have shoes to put on?	Yes	No
Do I have the ability to walk on my own?	Yes	No
Do I have vision?	Yes	No
Do I have a place to live?	Yes	No
Do I have family members to talk to?	Yes	No
Do I have friends to talk to?	Yes	No
Do I care for others?	Yes	No
Do I smile often?	Yes	No
Do I have the ability to read?	Yes	No
Do I have a job/career or have the ability to find one?	Yes	No
Do I have the mental capacity to function?	Yes	No
Do I have food to eat?	Yes	No
Do I have the ability to be creative?	Yes	No
Other: _____	Yes	No
Other: _____	Yes	No
Other: _____	Yes	No
Other: _____	Yes	No

Who are you?

I am nice to others.	Yes	No
I love myself.	Yes	No
I love my family.	Yes	No
I love my friends.	Yes	No
I like the simple things in life.	Yes	No
I breathe on my own.	Yes	No
I always give my best effort.	Yes	No
I know what I am good at.	Yes	No
I have a unique skill that no one knows about.	Yes	No
I am responsible.	Yes	No
People count on me.	Yes	No
I am a role model.	Yes	No
I have a great imagination.	Yes	No
I am a problem solver.	Yes	No
I am a fast learner.	Yes	No
I have a passion for something.	Yes	No
I know what I have a passion for.	Yes	No

What situations in your life do you want to change?

_____

_____

What are some of the thoughts you have had with yourself because of the situations you mentioned?

_____

_____

What are some ways to think positively about the situation(s)?

_____

_____

What are some positive thoughts about yourself?

_____

_____

What steps will you take to begin the process of thinking positive thoughts?

_____

_____

Benefits of Positive Thinking:

Pursue Your Purpose, Not Your Dream

Lesson 6   FACING THE POSSIBILITIES OF LIFE

Lesson Focus: This lesson will focus on the impact that failures and pressures can have in life. You will be able to understand how failures can help you grow and fulfill the outcomes in your life.

Wise Word Work: Complete one of the Wise Words activities on page 5.

Illustrate the pressure(s) you experience on a daily basis in the space below. Ask a partner if he/she can identify the pressure simply by looking at your drawing.

The Positives & Negatives of Pressure:

Throughout this chapter, the author discusses ways pressure can be positive or negative. Complete the table below with the author's ideas in this chapter. Add to them with your own ideas.

Positives	Negatives

☆ *Star the ideas on which you agree with the author.*

Failure vs. Success:

Look on page 54. In which areas do you lack success?

_____

_____

Why do you think it is dangerous to become friends with failure?

_____

_____

How do you react to failure? How can failure pave the way to success?

_____

_____

Create a cartoon in the frames below illustrating how failure can pave the way to success. Get as creative as you want. Give it a title.

_____

Research the failures of 4 of the most successful people you know about from sports, business, past, or present. Complete the table below with the information you find. What do they all have in common?

Person	Failures	Success	Secret to Success

How can a focus on failures impede your journey toward discovering your purpose?

_____

_____

How can failure propel your progress on the journey to discovering your purpose?

_____

_____

WHO ultimately makes the decision about how you will handle failure?

_____

_____

Pursue Your Purpose, Not Your Dream

Lesson 7   CHECK YOURSELF

Lesson Focus: In this lesson, you will learn how the people you surround yourself with impact your habits and who you become over time. You will recognize the importance of surrounding yourself with who you want to be like later in life.

Wise Word Work: Complete one of the Wise Words activities on page 5.

"Check Yourself": Make a list of some of the things the author means by the phrase, "check yourself".

1. _____   2. _____   3. _____

4. _____   5. _____   6. _____

The journey to my purpose begins in my _____.

28

Who Am I?

Add adjectives to describe "who you are" around the circle.

What do you value?

Values are personal beliefs. Add values to the treasure chest below. Place those values most important to you inside the chest and those of less importance outside the chest.

What is YOUR Purpose?

To find your purpose, think about something you do that makes you happy, so much so that you would do it for free. As of today, what would you identify as your purpose?

Place your ideas on the sign posts below.

Write a paragraph describing your purpose as you understand it today and why you believe that it is your purpose.

_____

_____

_____

_____

_____

_____

_____

_____

Pursue Your Purpose, Not Your Dream

Lesson 8   **REBUILDING YOU**

Lesson Focus: In this lesson, you will focus on the concept of rebuilding. This lesson will help you understand that everyone may experience a time in life that may require rebuilding. When rebuilding, there are steps you can take to enrich the process for better outcomes.

Wise Word Work: Complete one of the Wise Words activities on page 5.

Defining Rebuilding:

Complete this sentence & lists 3 examples of "rebuilding".

Rebuilding is...

_____

_____

_____

3 Examples of Rebuilding in your life:

    1. _____

    2. _____

    3. _____

How can rebuilding make you fearful and excited all at the same time? Explain

_____

_____

_____

Rate YOUR feelings about rebuilding by placing an X where you belong on this continuum.

   FEARFUL -- CONFIDENT

What does FEAR stand for in your life?

Create your own acronym for FEAR. Then create an acronym for your way of fighting fear.

F -

E -

A -

R –

Draw/Create a symbol for the process of rebuilding.

Pursue Your Purpose, Not Your Dream

Lesson 9 **THE ISM'S OF LIFE**

Lesson Focus: In this lesson students will recognize the many ISM's of life. Students will be able to understand the negative impact that these ISM's hold and how to overcome and or understand the impact they hold.

Wise Word Work: Complete one of the Wise Words activities on page 5.

Impact of Ism's:

What does the author mean by the term, "ism"? Why is he discussing this in detail?

_____

_____

_____

_____

_____

Your "Ism's" of Life:

It is important to identify the "ism's" in your life as you notice them so that you can confront them head-on.

Which "ism's" are most prevalent in your life?

_____   _____

_____   _____

_____   _____

Analyzing Ism Impact:

Choose 3 "ism's" that you noted above. List the ism and then rate your awareness and understanding of the ism by placing an X on the appropriate location of the continuum.

1. _____

UNDERSTANDING ---------------------------------**MISCONCPETION**

2. _____

UNDERSTANDING ---------------------------------**MISCONCPETION**

3. _____

UNDERSTANDING ---------------------------------**MISCONCPETION**

Choose one of the "ism's" above. How would a misconception of this ism impact your journey toward pursuing your purpose?

_____

_____

_____

My "Ism" Attack Plan:

Now that you know about the "ism's" and have read about examples of people confronting them, what is YOUR plan of attack keep them at bay so they don't derail your progress toward purpose pursuit? Explain your action plan in detail based on the "ism's" most prevalent in your life.

_____

_____

_____

_____

_____

_____

_____

How will you know if you are successful with your plan?

_____

_____

_____

_____

Name at least 3 people in your life that could be helpful in working through your "ism's" with you. Explain why each would be helpful.

_____   _____

_____   _____

_____   _____

Pursue Your Purpose, Not Your Dream

Lesson 10   **BUILDING YOUR TEAM**

Lesson Focus: In this lesson, you will learn the importance of being a part of a team. You will be able to understand and recognize how a team can be positive and support you in your journey to fulfill your purpose.

Wise Word Work: Complete one of the Wise Words activities on page 5.

What are the most important things YOU would consider when building a great team?

_____

_____

_____

_____

_____

_____

_____

_____

Who is on your personal team? To get some ideas, see pages 108-110 in the text. After listing names of people on your team, place an X next to those on your team who are aligned to what you want in your life.

_____   _____

_____   _____

_____   _____

_____   _____

_____   _____

Have you ever had to "kick" someone off of your team? How would you go about doing this if it was needed?

_____

_____

_____

_____

Compare & Contrast Your Team:

Compare & contrast your team with a famous sports team using the Venn Diagram below.

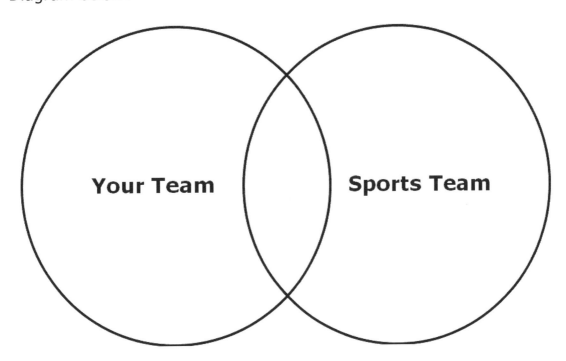

The 4 P's:

> **"You are a PRODUCT of the PEOPLE you PLACE in your PRESENCE!"**

Explain the meaning of the 4 P's in your own words.

_____
_____
_____
_____
_____
_____

Accountability:

All good team members (including you) need to be accountable.

Name 5 ways you keep yourself accountable.

1. _____
2. _____
3. _____
4. _____
5. _____

Team Mascot:

Most sports teams have mascots to symbolize who they are as a collective group. What would you choose for your team mascot to represent how your team functions together? Draw and label your mascot below with items that signify your team.

Pursue Your Purpose, Not Your Dream

Lesson 11   **DON'T GET IT TWISTED**

Lesson Focus: In this lesson, you will differentiate between purpose and dreams. You will be able to apply what you have learned throughout the entire book concerning your own purpose.

Wise Word Work: Complete one of the Wise Words activities on page 5.

> **"No matter where you are from,**
>
> **your dreams are valid!"**

Explain the meaning of this quote in your own words?

_____

_____

_____

_____

Do you agree or disagree with this quote? Why?

_____

_____

_____

Recap:

Your Possible Dreams: **Your Purpose:**

_____   _____

_____   _____

_____   _____

_____   _____

Based on your everyday actions, have you been following dreams or pursuing your purpose, the reason you are alive today? Support your statement with evidence.

_____

_____

_____

_____

_____

_____

_____

_____

Draw a map of your journey so far. Place barriers where they have occurred, rough passage when there were tough times, team mates along the way, detours when you may have gotten off track, and so forth. Place your goal or purpose toward the end of the journey.

Pursue Your Purpose, Not Your Dream

Lesson 12   CONCLUSION

Lesson Focus: This lesson will help you wrap up your thoughts related to next steps in pursuing your purpose rather than your dreams.

Wise Word Work: Complete one of the Wise Words activities on page 5.

Asking for Help:

Why do you think asking for help is so difficult for many people?

_____

_____

When do you typically ask for help? To whom do you ask?

_____

_____

_____

_____

_____

Why does the author say it is important to be able to ask for help?

_____

_____

_____

_____

Pride:

What is pride and how can it be a barrier to making progress on your journey?

_____

_____

_____

_____

_____

Write about a time when you were too proud to ask for help. Describe the outcome.

_____

_____

_____

_____

_____

_____

_____

_____

_____

_____

Describe what you learned from this experience.

_____

_____

_____

_____

_____

_____

My Next Steps:

What were the KEY elements learned from *Pursue Your Purpose?* What next steps will YOU take in your journey to pursue YOUR purpose?

What I Knew	What I Learned	My Goal	Small Steps to Reach Success	End Goal (Success)

My Purpose Pathway Checklist

How do I know if I am "pursuing my purpose"?

Check all that apply today.

☐ I train for my long distance run by doing things now to prepare myself along the way.

☐ I take time to know myself.

☐ My actions and values are aligned.

☐ I am comfortable with the uncomfortable.

☐ I have built a solid team to support me.

☐ I think an speak positively.

☐ I take steps to overcome fear.

☐ I ask for help as needed.

☐ I have a clear understanding of "ism's".

☐ I have changed to why I think about purpose and dreams.

☐ I have moved beyond "cool".

☐ I am focused pursuing my purpose rather than society's dreams.

Pairing this checklist of behaviors is a great way to track your own progress in pursuing your purpose! The Purpose Pathway rubric on the next page provides a way for you to measure your progress.

My Purpose Pathway Rubric

Student Name:

_____

Date:

_____

Daily Goal:

_____

1 – displayed **very few or no** behaviors enabling pursuit of my purpose.

2 – displayed **a few** behaviors enabling pursuit of my purpose.

3 – displayed **several** behaviors enabling pursuit of my purpose.

4 – displayed **many** behaviors enabling pursuit of my purpose.

Complete and initial the Self Rating (S). Ask your teacher complete and initial the Teacher Rating (T).

Teacher/Period	Monday	Tuesday	Wednesday	Thursday	Friday	Total
Self	1 2 3 4	1 2 3 4	1 2 3 4	1 2 3 4	1 2 3 4	S =
Teacher	1 2 3 4	1 2 3 4	1 2 3 4	1 2 3 4	1 2 3 4	T =
Self	1 2 3 4	1 2 3 4	1 2 3 4	1 2 3 4	1 2 3 4	S =
Teacher	1 2 3 4	1 2 3 4	1 2 3 4	1 2 3 4	1 2 3 4	T =
Self	1 2 3 4	1 2 3 4	1 2 3 4	1 2 3 4	1 2 3 4	S =
Teacher	1 2 3 4	1 2 3 4	1 2 3 4	1 2 3 4	1 2 3 4	T =
Self	1 2 3 4	1 2 3 4	1 2 3 4	1 2 3 4	1 2 3 4	S =
Teacher	1 2 3 4	1 2 3 4	1 2 3 4	1 2 3 4	1 2 3 4	T =
Self	1 2 3 4	1 2 3 4	1 2 3 4	1 2 3 4	1 2 3 4	S =
Teacher	1 2 3 4	1 2 3 4	1 2 3 4	1 2 3 4	1 2 3 4	T =
Self	1 2 3 4	1 2 3 4	1 2 3 4	1 2 3 4	1 2 3 4	S =
Teacher	1 2 3 4	1 2 3 4	1 2 3 4	1 2 3 4	1 2 3 4	T =
Self	1 2 3 4	1 2 3 4	1 2 3 4	1 2 3 4	1 2 3 4	S =
Teacher	1 2 3 4	1 2 3 4	1 2 3 4	1 2 3 4	1 2 3 4	T =
Self	1 2 3 4	1 2 3 4	1 2 3 4	1 2 3 4	1 2 3 4	S =
Teacher	1 2 3 4	1 2 3 4	1 2 3 4	1 2 3 4	1 2 3 4	T =
Self	1 2 3 4	1 2 3 4	1 2 3 4	1 2 3 4	1 2 3 4	S =
Teacher	1 2 3 4	1 2 3 4	1 2 3 4	1 2 3 4	1 2 3 4	T =

**Graph your data to view clearer results!

Student Name:_____

Parent Signature: _____

Journey to MY PURPOSE

Document YOUR "*Journey to MY PURPOSE*". Note defining moments in your life that have helped you to recognize your movement on this journey. Based on your goals, place future defining moments when these goals will be successfully completed.

CONGRATULATIONS,

_____

ON

COMPLETING YOUR PORTFOLIO:

MY PURPOSE PATHWAYS!

_____   _____

_____   _____

Made in the USA
Middletown, DE
09 September 2015